Writing on the Wall
Toxteth Library
Windsor Street, Liverpool
L8 1XF

Published by Writing on the Wall, 2021

Edited by The Liverpool Editing Company
Design and layout by Katrina Paterson

ISBN: 978-1-910580-50-9

0151 703 0020
info@writingonthewall.org.uk
www.writingonthewall.org.uk

**Stay up to date with our latest books,
projects, courses, and events with
our newsletter. Sign up on our website
writingonthewall.org.uk**

Contents

Danielle McLauren

Deborah Williams

Gary English

Introduction

'One idea that comes through loud and clear in this remarkable book is that people matter, supporting each other in extreme times is what gets us through, knowing we are giving back to another.'

Deborah Morgan,
author, and *Write Minds* Tutor.

What's Your Story? Write Minds is a result of the impact the Covid 19 pandemic and lockdown has had on mental health and wellbeing, amidst loneliness, job insecurity, relationship breakdowns, bereavements and a fundamental change to the pattern of our lives. According to a June 2020 study by the mental health charity *Mind,* 60% of adults and 68% of young people saw their mental health and wellbeing decline over the lockdown period. Feedback from our project participants demonstrates the positive impact creativity can have on the mental health and wellbeing on people's lives: *'There were elements of Lockdown which left me feeling terrified, Writing on the Wall changed that'.*

Writing on the Wall's *What's Your Story?* project has been running for over a decade. In that time we have published anthologies of the work of

I

hundreds of participants, all sharing their unique experiences; from being a part of the criminal justice system, to experiencing human trafficking, from stroke survivors, to young carers and people suffering domestic abuse.

This collection, which represents a beacon of hope, of human connection and radical change, shines a light on participants' experiences of isolation and its effect on their mental health and wellbeing as a result of living through lockdown. The stories within this anthology may make you laugh out loud, or pause you to reflect in the quiet, relatable moments, and sometimes it will stop you in your tracks.

Thank you to the Writing on the Wall staff who brought this project to life and who work tirelessly to keep projects like this going, especially throughout the lockdown.

I'd like to say a special thank you to our *Write Minds* course leader, Deborah Morgan, author and playwright, who imparted her own knowledge and invaluable advice to the writers, and fostered an encouraging environment and place of safety to allow the writers to flourish in telling their own stories.

I would like to offer our congratulations and thanks to the writers who took part in *Write Minds*, who are published for the first time in this moving and inspiring anthology. Thank you for continually showing up and allowing yourselves to be honest and vulnerable in your work and telling your stories as only you can, and for the generosity you gave to each other week after week. It was a privilege to be a part of such a special group of writers and this anthology is a testament to this. I hope you enjoy reading this collection as much as I have. Keep on writing!

Lauren Buxton
Project Worker
Writing on the Wall

What's Your Story?
Write Minds

Marks and Spencer Pyjamas

Ange Woolf

Admittedly, they were comfortable. I could sit around in them at home and not notice I had them on. Soft edges, faded cartoon animal prints and threadbare in places from years of washing, but I wouldn't answer the door in them! As I loaded the washing machine, I realised this was true of all my nightwear; old, misshapen, comfortable, but pretty unappealing to look at. I did not realise exactly how worn, some may even have said scruffy, until I saw my friend at home one day in her matching two piece, and seemingly new nightwear. I had a moment of envy as I saw how she was able to answer the door in hers without embarrassment.

I remember seeing the same sort of pyjamas she wore on a showroom dummy in the window of Marks and Spencer in town, elegantly printed navy blue and white striped silk material. I wondered what sort of home life you would have if you bought those sorts of pyjamas. I always walked past these windows with their classy pyjamas; they seemed to be clothing that would be worn by other people with other lives. I could imagine wearing them, but not in the life I was currently in.

The thing is money wasn't easy. I budgeted with what I was given. 'Housekeeping' he called it. We always had nice food and drinks and an occasional takeaway, but apart from that, no extras. I remembered when I had to really put my foot down about a holiday. Not a foreign holiday, but a local one, just something so we'd been away. It caused problems, but I made it happen. I can't fully blame him, he did the best he could, but he was not known for his generosity with money. I know he thought he was generous as we had a home and the bills were paid for, and this was something that didn't go unnoticed by me, but what also got noticed was the constant comments on how much things cost, how he actively wouldn't go somewhere expensive on principle, and how we missed out on a great deal of events as a result.

Any money I ended up with, as extra from my work, went on the children's Christmas presents and cinema trips. He'd never pay for these. 'Why pay to watch a film in the cinema when you could download it at home for free?' he'd ask. He never understood the experience of the cinema, nor why a large-screened, professionally filmed film would be more enjoyable for me than a handheld cam version streamed off his laptop. The arts weren't his thing either, come to think of it; he saw it as 'non-essential'. New clothes were the height of luxury, and I didn't buy them often.

I had never really considered what I looked like in the evenings or at weekends when at home until now. I wore nice enough clothes for work or the pub, but at home, I saw it as my 'down time'. Time for me to relax. And, after all, my husband never commented, he loved me for whatever I wore, so I didn't need to make any effort. Sitting there in my washed-out clothes, I thought about my pyjamas, then my friend's pyjamas.

I thought about our respective marriages - and there it was, like a large penny the size of a plate had dropped. I didn't make the effort because it didn't matter. The thought struck at my heart. The shop window pyjamas were for people who wanted to look nice at home and I didn't. Pyjamas tumbled around in the machine, all flopping on top of one another, left then right. Why didn't I see this until now? I guess time just moves so quickly with small children, pyjamas had been the last thing on my mind, but so had my own heart's desires. The tears rolled now, the feeling you get when you look yourself in the eye and accept something unpleasant, a mixture of shame and guilt.

I was right all along, though. Those pyjamas were not for me; at least, not yet!

H.O.L.L.A.N.D
Ange Woolf

It is early. Probably too early to be awake, but time seemed to move differently here. I was different, too. The bed isn't mine, but it didn't feel strange. It felt right, like a version of a potential future. The room, a mixture of light and dark, running out of hours. It would be time to leave soon. I roll over and check the time, four hours until our flight. Your back is to me, your dark hair messed up, scratches on your back. We couldn't get enough of one another, but sex was merely the expression of that feeling, way beneath that was what really counted, we couldn't get enough of each other's time, hands, faces and most importantly, minds.

I trace your spine with one finger, you shudder and roll over to face me. We both smile, as if in a mixture of shyness and surprise; there we were, away together, and in a different country.

Holland. I had never been before now. It made me think of the Valentine cards that I used to write in the 70s, S.W.A.L.K, (Sealed With A Loving Kiss), how profound it seemed to be, professing your feelings independently onto a card for the boy you liked. H.O.L.L.A.N.D, (Hope Our love Lasts And Never Dies). I thought of this as I looked at your face. I don't think I had ever loved anyone so much before. This feeling was not just for you, it was for me too, like self-love. You were good for me, you wanted what was best for me. I had never experienced that kind of care since my mum.

If only. This is all that went through my mind. If only we'd met sooner, if only we didn't have to snatch time, if only we could be together, always. The elephant in the room was not fierce nor large. It was a cuddly one with no tusks, and it sat on the table in the corner of the room, along with our passports. It was the gift I had to promise to bring back when I prised my daughter out of my arms and into her dad's as she wept. I did too. Cuddly toys were always good currency when buying time away from her. The guilt I felt as I walked out of the house to get a bus to the airport was stomach-churning, but I knew what the alternative was; to shrivel up and melt into the background of the mushroom coloured paint on each wall. A job lot bought cheap.

I had made up my mind what I needed to do but not quite how to do it. Being honest with my husband about our marriage being broken was one of the hardest things I ever had to do, apart from agreeing to the turning off of the life support machine on my mum. This pain was equal but not with the same outcome, but grief is grief. He cried, I did too, but we both knew we were making one another unhappy, and sometimes, our lives don't need to end while they're still being lived.

I get up, feeling the familiar dread of the weekend

coming to an end. I pull on my silk navy blue and white striped Marks and Spencer pyjamas that I had bought especially for the trip, the ones that I would never have bought for home and I put the small kettle on, run the hot water in the bath while it boils, then perch on the side. I look at you, stretching and scratching, singing as you did, and I promised myself that I would do it. I would get the life that I needed. After all, I already had the pyjamas.

And in the end
Ange Woolf

I put the clothes into the bin bag along with the shoes, bags and miscellany that was already in and on their way to finding a new home via the local charity shop. I found it hard to let go of things. It was a mixture of believing they would come in handy again another year down the line (hoarding instinct inherited from my dad) and a feeling of guilt due to the mass consumption of goods in the western worlds (socialist politics inherited from my mum). As I reached for the next pile of clothes destined for the bag, I came across the Marks and Spencer pyjamas.

Navy blue and white stripes, the silk, threadbare from wear and washing. It was hard not to smile when I looked at them. I could see every hotel, every snuggled-up night on the couch and every night of passion that they had seen. They had a few holes around the waistline and the elastic was showing through, but despite this, they had still maintained their shape and colour, due to being good quality. They'd lasted four years, despite seeing a lot of action - previous night wear looked ruined in a shorter space of time, but that was because it was cheap. Cheap materials churned out by underage children no doubt, all that effort and sweat, only for them to be fit for the charity shop within the year. It was expensive being poor, as my mum used to say.

I held the pyjamas up to the light. They should go into the bin bag really. I didn't hold on to stuff anymore like that, didn't have to, as I knew I could buy another good pair if I wanted to, but I still wasn't quite used to the fact that I was in charge of my own finances and made my own decisions.

These pyjamas were coming to the end of their day, and it was OK to recycle them, but these were the pyjamas that other people wore, but they had become mine, the life that other happier people led had become mine. Now, I was the person with good quality pyjamas who could answer the door of her new home in decent nightwear and whose children didn't need to miss her when she'd gone because there was nothing to escape from anymore. Everything I needed was right here.

Bird's eye
Ange Woolf

'Street trash
Flying rat
Spreader of germs
Not eater of worms
Nor pretty of wing
No song to sing'
I know you think this

But you have never been taught or shown
The love that exists before we've flown
a bond that grows
from egg to flight
racer or homer
street bird or roller
just listen closely
hear our warm coo
hold us to your breast
and feel it too
then let us go
and watch us soar
camouflaged grey by the Mersey

The floor
sees our half-broken feet from your lack of care
a few seconds more
is all it would take

to brake, or step sideways
These streets
we can share

Miles apart
Ange Woolf

How hard a thing to do
to not reach out and comfort you
Here we stood
miles apart
view through a windowpane
pain from the longing
Not separated by birth
but by two metres worth
The distance feels wrong
Too hard to see through
The need for touch and comfort
especially for you
A few days later I touched your face
your arms outstretched; we closed the space
I held your body close and tight
our world at last, was put to right

Beneath the surface
Ange Woolf

You enter the water
your grey coat grows darker
shallow at first,
you stumble
as cold rushes into your stockings,
your pockets,
heavier with each step,
the rocks you carry
returning to the river
you slip again,
beneath the surface
which in your mind,
was always the deep end.

Let us discuss despair, swiftly
Ange Woolf

Your pain, like mine
clouds our eyes
as shadows melt and hush the light
and darkness comes to bruise the sky

Meanwhile

The rain hydrates
seeds germinate
songs from birds
strike perfect chords
and colour is its own reward
let us close this darkened door
And rise to grace
With voices clear
Feet firm in place

We are here

There is a light that never goes out
Ange Woolf

Options are fading
people are trying
piling on platitudes
jaded of meaning

You're giving up

You can't let them in
safely trapped
no second sight or electric light
to guide you through the endless night

You have to believe me when I say
that night can swiftly turn to day
the shadows that now blind your mind
will soon be gone
as light can find
its way into the darkest reaches
experience comes at times to teach us

Bottling up
Ange Woolf

I track and trace my own bad days
Add them to my database
Extract the essence from each fall
bottle them, however small
label them upon my shelf
With the title 'Mental Health'
Then when I'm well and feeling good,
Not anxious or misunderstood
I'll open up the biggest one
Allow it out, to spill and run
to see how darkness stole those days
and how my mind was all ablaze
then scoop it up and put it back
safely sealed without a crack
and note how transience is life
and peace is equal to the strife
I'll hold on tight to faith and hope
even when I cannot cope
and watch my strength, see how I rise
and grow despite the silent cries
I recognise I'm not defeated
I throw my arms out wide to greet, that
everything will be all right
Because I'm still here to put it right

The Mental Load
Ange Woolf

How does she find
the space in her mind
to write down what she has to say?
A room of her own would be a good start
but mere walls will not keep it at bay

The mental load
The enemy within
more so than sheer lack of space
The call of the wild
will drag her each time
to return to her mothering place

She must find the drive
that blocks out all time
and the will to put all else aside
to get it on paper
those words that escape her
perfection and editing can slide

Once down on the page
her sorrow, her rage
can be tidied, corrected, and sorted
but 'til she makes time
to spew forth her mind
her writing dreams will always be thwarted

Breaking News
Bretta Kane

A friend said she knew it was over when her aunt gave her a teapot for one, that she'd won at the bingo. Another, when she realised the Sky Sports subscription had been cancelled.

My enlightenment came when only one Sunday newspaper landed on the hall mat.

Carol, the newsagent, knew before me.

Sat on the bottom stair, I could no longer deny the headlines in front of me

that break had now become broken

Our unspoken differences

Mirrored in his choice, mine spread out across the bed

left him no room in the relationship, he said.

Perhaps there was a warning written in the stars you read, but I gave no credit to the incompatible signs

Me busy keeping up with the times, failing to read between the lines,

Or see the issues spelt out in the unwritten text

You the silent observer

Never a crossword word, true, you hated them,

seems you were far better at cryptic clues than I'd realised.

Kevin
Bretta Kane

Kevin - that's what she calls me
A small face pressed up against the glass
Her pink rimmed eyes meet mine
And a secret understanding passes between us
Both blown off course, our internal compasses broken
Her breathy sighs form small clouds that
trapped, like me
cannot rise to join others in the sky
Displaced, our dreams are the same
Me homing - now homeless, her daughter - now
ward
Striving for survival in unfamiliar surroundings
She envies my freedom, I her sanctuary
She too carries the heavy weight of others'
expectations
Once wedded to the man, I wear his ring
though unshackled, I still feel the pull of the chain
from a distance
Freedom comes at a price
I was his hopes and dreams, he travelled with me,
He too is caged

Absence
Bretta Kane

This photograph hangs in my hall along with many other family snaps. I walk past it several times a day but don't really see it.

Although I feel the love and warmth generated by the force that is my family, it's more what I didn't see on that day, which is so obvious to me now. It's the *absence* of someone that shouts out and saddens me. Someone who deliberately avoided being part of the family group.

I remember the joyous weekend spent together. It was no mean feat to gather all of us siblings all in one place; as adults we had scattered across the globe. I can hear the children and some of the partners speaking in delightfully different accents, making us sound more Scouse than usual and the high octave of our raising voices as we revert to type and clamour to be heard over each other as we did as children. Still fighting for attention.

I love the randomness, the informality of it, no one organised us, the group formed organically. A picture woven and interlocked with a shared familial history, not all born into the family but carefully chosen or who chose to be part of the rich tapestry.

What the photograph can't tell me is *why*. Was she afraid the camera would capture her intentions, reveal her secrets?

Her disappearing act had started well before this was taken, but it was done by stealth and I'd failed to see the signs.

Remains of the day
Bretta Kane

In the darkness, I plunge my hands into the murky waters of the night and try to scour away the fetid remnants of the day.

Self-worth as delicate as china, is chipped away, voices and harsh opinions eddy together and ripple up through the water, gathering volume.

Invisible cracks leave me fragile and easily damaged, the mantra etched into the pattern repeats my nightmare, adds weight to the belief that echoes inside my head - I do not deserve to be loved.

As night fades, the dirty water draining from the sink, revealing the porcelain whiteness of morning, drags down my fears with it.

But like the greasy tidemark and stubborn residue the fairy cannot remove, the deepest stains remain.

Filled up again with clean water of the dawn dew every dirty dish of insults, cup of casual dismissal served up to me that day goes in to soak away the hurt and await the night time ritual of cleansing my soul performed in the lonely kitchen of my mind.

And I wait to be broken again.

SOLACE
Bretta Kane

You're leaving again
Signalled by the growing distance between us
I feel your restlessness, the warmth has faded from
your fire
Pale-faced, shame-faced, with some kindness, a nod
to what we shared
you recede slowly
so, I can adjust to the dark days ahead and cling to
the memory of your image
burnt onto the lids of my closed eyes
You'll move on to caress the exposed skin and limbs
of new lovers
Kiss the necks of others, as you used to mine
seduce them into thinking this love affair will last
As Earth's axis tilts
the gravitational pull of distant shores too strong
for you to resist
I wait until again I feel your presence
For I know you will continue to return until the end
of time

Carriers
Bretta Kane

Fleet footed Hermes, now messenger of the Goods
Amazon smiles, made from the rainforest woods
Sweet song of Yodel, the power of Parcel Force
Electronic highway men perform the humane cause
shades of Saharian sand, Tibetan tea, the glint of
Stormzy's crown
taupe taped, ecru enveloped ranging from beige to
brown
This Dulux palette, new additions to the colour chart
reinforced, corrugated, shape this new form of art
They bridge the old to our brave new world
We track and trace, anticipate
what wonders to unfurl
A van, a man, rings the bell then bids a hasty retreat
Thumbs up behind glass, the two cannot meet

Williamson Square Residents
Danielle McLauren

Nestled into the nooks and crevices of monuments
finding stone shelter in buildings, the chill of the
Irish Sea
carried to the city's heart on the Mersey wind

We stop here a while and watch the waves
of fast-walkers, talkers, plodders, observers;
a criss-cross of loose threads, stories intertwining

In collaboration with the street busker
chatter flutters up to the gutters where we perch
Catching our chances from an open wrapper,
cold chips beckon us to the patchwork of damp
flagstones
Our flight is welcomed with high-pitched yelps
hands and feet shooing us away

Springing back to the misty grey above
dissatisfaction and a single scrap caught in our beaks
we release our objection onto the heads below

The Call
Danielle McLauren

This morning, they had been in a rush. Nothing had been prepped the night before – no lunches made, no uniforms ironed, no shoes laid out in the hallway with laces untied. Plus, the alarm didn't ring as loudly as normal, she was sure of it. All in all, the hour between 7 and 8am caused high levels of anxiety, and Mira was already exhausted.

Closing the door after dropping her little darlings off, she sank onto the sofa with a sigh, and allowed her eyelids to flutter shut. Just twenty minutes, she thought to herself.

The telephone ringing made her jump, yanking her out of a disturbing dream. Still half asleep, she fumbled around down the side of the sofa to where the phone usually lived, letting her hands be guided by the incessant ringing.

'Hello?' she said.

Nothing.

'Hello? Mira speaking.'

Still nothing. She pressed the cancel button, presuming someone else had experienced a similarly stressful morning and dialled the wrong number. Pinching her cheeks and shaking her head like a wet dog in an attempt to muster up energy to continue with her day, the silence was broken yet again by the telephone ringing.

'Hello?'

'You have twenty seconds to get out. 20, 19, 18, 17...' said a raspy voice. The confusion and mounting fear began to claw its way over Mira's skin, as her brain desperately began to scramble for a logical explanation.

'Who is this?'

'15, 14...'

'I will call the police!'

'12, 11, 10, 9...'

Mira's eyes darted around the room, then out of the window, desperate for some clue. Realising that the voice on the other end had just said the number three, Mira realised that she had left it too late.

'2, 1.'

Bittersweet
Danielle McLauren

I learnt about two major things at the age of seven:
sex and inflation
Sex, I discovered, was something to do with babies
and love
but not to be talked about when Sue and Mike were
round for dinner
I was okay with that
Inflation hit me harder
Memories of my last visit just one month prior
had me salivating before I had even opened the
sticker-laden door
Peach floor tiles decorated with the muddy footprints
of my fellow classmates gone before me on that rainy
day in April
A kaleidoscope of sugary treats at the back hit my
eyes as the smell of Flumps and Spaceships and
Lollipops and Bon Bons painted a smile on my
freckled face
The 20p warm in my sweaty hand,
I watched Jas shovel the Fizzy Cola Bottles into the
flimsy paper bag
She stopped at ten
I waited for her to start again
but all she did was hand me the bag in exchange for
that 20p piece
I can still taste my disappointment at the true value

of that coin

The Sun, My Love
Danielle McLauren

When you leave, an ache hovers behind my eyes
    that reminds me of the endless nights when I
only have myself to wipe my tears.
    I try to recall the feeling of your kiss dancing on
my pearly skin, dashing it with speckles of terracotta.
    The sweetness of that solar caress, filling me up
with youthful audacity.

For too long, you have come and gone
    without a single thought for what your presence
and absence do to my soul.
    You have slept behind the blanket of clouds then
exploded back into my days,
    smug in the knowledge that I won't be able to
withhold a smile when I see you again.
    You know your worth like only a god can.
    I want to rise up against you and demand a little
more respect.
    I want to declare that I have embraced the dull
and misty hours when you hide from my sight and
that I don't need you anymore.
    I want to not need you anymore.

But I am living and breathing, and my existence
revolves around you, of that I must admit.
    I guess I will simply say goodbye until I see you

once more.

And I will smile when we meet again, like always.

Rocks In My Pocket
Danielle McLauren

The first time is the worst time
they say
for having your heart broken
I cried enough to fill the reservoir
swore to wrap myself in some sort of shield
I was eight years old
Mum promised me I would smile again
because a heart can't be broken, just dismantled

When my bones stopped aching
and my soul no longer bled
she gave me a pebble
Cold, smooth, the colour of the almost-forgotten bits
of sky at sunset
I was to hold this little rock
to remember that whatever happens
I won't always hurt

At eleven years old
I experienced my first last goodbye
Surrounded by pain and grief
I wanted to float away and return to a world of games
and stories
Somehow, the weight of that tiny pebble kept my
feet on the ground
long enough to make it through the funeral, at least

Aged twenty-seven
when I lay in hospital hearing the news that my
chances of being called "Mummy"
were being cut away with the removal of each
damaged piece of ovary
my morphine riddled fingers clasped that pebble

Now, the cases rise
lives are on pause
dreams packed away for a later date
a cancelled Christmas
Still, shoved deep in the pocket of my jeans
is that little piece of this planet
telling me that everything's going to be alright
We won't always hurt

Tough Love
Danielle McLauren

Waking up is hard
Lying in bed in the dark
with only your own breath
and the loose threads of memories of another
is hard
Having a dream that rips down the middle
learning that your face does not fit their idea
or that your hips do not fit into those jeans;
sitting at a table eating a meal, surrounded on all
sides
feeling like not one single word or glance is for you
is hard
Closing the door behind you
being greeted by nothing but the worn-out rug
beneath your feet
and the sound of emptiness
is hard

My mother taught me that 'anyway' was the only
way
Life is hard, but I have to believe *anyway*
I have to believe that
even when the darkness hacks its way into my safe
place
even when my own hands are around my throat
and the last marble of hope starts its descent

the drapes can be pulled back to let the light in
I have to believe that one day, I will turn the tapestry
over
the tangled loose threads of wasted chances and
disappointments no longer visible
and I will see that all this time
    I have been weaving something beautiful.

A Kind of Bad Day

Danielle McLauren

We are all in the same boat, they say. We are all in this crazy game of life together. When she was five years old, a boy in her class who wore the same clothes for four weeks, scratched her face and laughed when she cried. But her mother told her that she was called to be kind, no matter what. She told her that we can't fully know the pain that someone might be feeling, and we need to remember that we are all just humans who want to be loved, deep down. So, just be kind.

On days like today, however, when her hangover is doing that tap-dance on her head and crawling up her throat, when her 'sent' messages are cruel reminders of new lows that she hit last night and when her neighbour is playing Shania Twain's 'Man, I Feel Like a Woman' for the seventh time since 7.44 this morning, kindness is not on her mind. In fact, what she really wants to do, what will really solve the current problem, is murder. She can simply knock on the door and as Daniel Delacruz swings it open in all his sweaty glory (this is his cleaning song so she knows he'll be sweating), she can plunge a knife deep into his all-too-often bare chest. Or crack him over the head with her 3kg yet-unused kettlebell. But the mere thought of exercise makes the Malbec vomit rise a little higher, so she swiftly suppresses all murder plans. She is far too hungover for murder today. Instead, she composes as 'kind' a text as she can muster.

Hi Dan, hate to be an arse, but I'm dying with a hangover! Any chance you can turn the music down?

She waits for a response. After the ninth time Shania belts out that song, the realisation that he might not be near his phone dawns on her. She peels her mascara-streaked face off the pillow and somehow manages to find herself on her feet. Dragging herself towards the front door, on the way out, she picks up that 3kg kettlebell.

In Good Company
Danielle McLauren

'Whoever you are, no matter how lonely,
The world offers itself to your imagination.'

From Wild Geese by Mary Oliver

In me is me, us, we
Pockets filled with possibilities
Today, I sit motionless, with nothing but my breath
tomorrow, I am hurtling through the valley of a land
unknown
I may make just one cup of coffee in the morning
hear only my footsteps as I wander along the river
I may not feel the curve of my back pressed against
the warmth of someone's skin at night
but the stories that hold my hand
drown out the sound of loneliness
The thoughts of protagonists
the dreams of queens
the downfalls and victories
of those that I paint with my words
sit with me at the table and dance with me in the
kitchen.
These are the voices that sing me to sleep
give me that goodnight kiss
to keep me from falling into an abyss.

Lockdown: Those Middle Months

Danielle McLauren

You're a cup of tea brewed for too long
Murky, saturated, the film of stale water floating
on the top

The tangled, matted hair of your head
potential of beauty wrapped in a tatty bobble

I sip you, burning my tongue
yet wrapping my fingers around your warmth

Your heart is a tired mother, nursing her baby at 4am
Her cries pierce you, claw at her insides

A towering silver-back deep in the jungle
possessing a strength and protective wall

Like yellow Fruit Pastilles, you were welcomed and
feared
Now, on the brink again, we await your return.

Inoperable
Danielle McLauren

Sometimes, it is lodged between my tonsils -
attempts to swallow thwarted by the mass that is
stuck
Other times, it sits on my chest -
not heavy enough to stop me breathing
but I learn to live by shallow inhalations all the same
It claws its way down my belly
takes up space where roast dinners with family
and pizza on the couch with my love should be
It covers my skin
letting nothing and no one in

The world offers cures
none of which I can afford
Not now, anyway
Too often I have pulled myself onto the precipice of
a life shared
only to have my fingertips stamped on
I have stood and smiled into the face of another
only to be shown a mirror
so that I stare at my scars

Escape plans and numbing strategies are futile
nowadays
It still swells and presses and burns when the voices
don't stop and when they disappear

That's the problem with loneliness
None of it really matters.

She Turned off the Lawnmower
Deborah Williams

She turns the lawnmower off.

'I've finished, going in to do my face. I've been thinking...'

I look up from my task of clearing the dead flowers from the borders of our garden. I glance around, taking in the two apple blossom trees we planted when we first moved in, the trellis by the door; you built that with Grace when she was little. It's so weathered now that it's only the greedy stems of the clematis stopping it from falling to bits. It's Mum's favourite place to sit, caught in the paradox of being present and absent at the same time.

'It's just, well - it's just that I wanted you to know that everything is going to be okay, you know, Mum.'

I try to hide my surprise. I even manage to turn the corners of my mouth up. It's enough; she's satisfied. I watch her walk back into the house. My Grace, her blue-green hair a waterfall down her back. She's dyed it so often I've almost forgotten her natural colour. An image of her as a toddler comes to me, hair in a sweet bob the colour of a Seaforth Sand's sunset.

I look down at my pink cleaning gloves covered in earth and bits of dead petunias. I've never enjoyed the feel of soil between my fingers, all gritty and tenacious under my nails. I'm a reluctant gardener.

I enjoy the colourful flowers and put up with the work needed to achieve them.

She is choosing to be positive. It is the new religion after all, negativity now a mortal sin. I am usually a devout follower. I have many self-help books, even read most of them. Positivity, optimism, I had it in spadefuls when I was her age, through heartbreak and loss, and I never doubted things would get better. But I now know that was 'youth', and 'youth' has a resilience that comes from thinking you have endless time. But that is something I don't have.

I stare down at the dead, decaying mess of the once-vibrant plant in my hands, its roots still caked in soil. It's only recently that I realised what soil actually is - the rotted transmuted remains of everything that has ever lived. It fascinates and repels me that something made up of death can create so much life, over and over again. Grief mugs me with a punch to the stomach and crumples me in two.

'Mum, d'you want herbal or normal tea? You okay?'

'Yeah, yes. Just backache, all this bending. Peppermint, please.'

I sit back on my hunches, scrub my eyes with a clean part of my arm and check my watch. We have an hour until the scheduled call to the hospital.

We can't visit you or hold your hand - COVID has taken this away. You can't see us. Your eyes have been closed for a week now. A kind, muffled-voiced nurse holds the phone in front of your face, and we tell you virtually that we love you, to get better, to come home soon. You don't respond and I fear you have already left us.

Isolation, loneliness, they were here long before lockdown, closed cafes and pubs make little difference to my routine. Through years of Mum's complex, complicated illness we coped, pushed through and coped.

Dementia, death by the cruellest increments. Invisible carers they call us and it's true; I feel transparent. But I don't know if I can cope with what comes next. I can't control it, or fix it and this year, this bloody year...

Grace hands me the mug she bought me for Mother's Day. 'If mums were flowers, I'd pick you'.

'Thanks love, I'll be in soon. We can make a start on tea before we call the hospital.'

'No need, I'm doing pasta and pesto, it's nearly ready, I'll shout you.'

She walks away. She doesn't cry and I worry over that. I've tried to tell her that I can carry her pain with mine. But she is young and trying to tread softly around me and I couldn't love her more.

Placing the cup at my side, hands shaking, I rip my gloves off and plunge my hands deep into the soil. The rich thick earth so full of life pushes into my nails, and I knead and turn the earth, pushing it in further still.

Daystar
Deborah Williams

Gaia has fulfilled her promise
her fruits picked, the tilled soil rests
and the spent fields lie in the misty embrace of
autumn

You have brought about this change
Ra, Apollo worshipped as a god
Magnetic, fiery, I try to resist. But your presence
pervades my world
only the shadow can dispel it
there I avoid you, so afraid of being
burned by your gaze

Here I wait, between fear and yearning
aching to feel radiant and enlivened by you
Undeterred, the Cosmic wheel turns in its eternal
covenant, pulling you further and further from me
The shadow grows
It is your absence I feel the most
You depart, I remain desolate without you

Abled
Gary English

The child in the café
shouted nonsense at the top of his voice
above playground sounds from outside
And they laughed at his joy
His wheelchair sat at the same table each day
As his dad fed him chips
Tenderly wiping his mouth as required
The love in his eyes
Reflected in laughter
As the boy shouted sounds
At the top of his voice

Two tables down
Sat a man, with a man
Feeding him cake
With coffee or tea
Tenderly wiping his mouth as required
As they talked about old times
But nothing quite new
As he never quite knew
If the present was true
They waved through the window
At the man and his dog
Though he couldn't see them
But a nudge from his wife made him turn with a
wave

and a smile

Two tables down
I sat alone with my breakfast
And I laughed with them all
As they laughed with the boy
And I waved at the man, with the wife and the dog
Though I know he is blind to my smile

Am I watching the world pass me by?
I don't know, I can't think
As I sip at my drink
Only half understanding my life
Through a haze I still gaze
Watching everyone smile with a genuine joy
For the man and the boy
And the father and son
For the man and his dog and his wife
And a tear half trickles
As I wish I was much more like them
Able
And stable
As I sit at the table
Two tables down from the door

About Cats
Gary English

I dream about cats.

I'm not a fan, preferring to take them or leave them. Take them out with a blunderbuss, I joke. Or leave them in other people's gardens, where they belong; not sneaking into mine as bold as daylight.

When I'm writing, sometimes, a cat walks by my window, all open and above board; head high, like a duchess. I know full well its final destination is my garden. To chase birds or lie in wait for half-tame squirrels, fed on nuts and seeds.

This riles me. My blood boils and I rap on the window, emitting some incoherent yell, like a victim in a dream, chased by monsters.

The cat pauses for a moment. And slowly turns its head; majestic in its motion. I'm sure it smiles and tuts. What can this agitated person want? Why does it interrupt my progress?

The neck twists slowly back and front paws rise and fall, like a dressage pony, processing on its way.

Frenzied, I leap out of my chair, screaming, without doubt, some wild profanity at the air, in lieu of the cat. Rushing to the back door, I leap out into the garden, wishing my water bucket full of rainwater, hoping the garden hose is still attached to the outside tap. It isn't of course. It's in the shed. With the bucket.

The cat escapes a soaking.

Besides. The cat is far smarter than I and disappears without trace before I unlock the door. Returning, probably, once I stumble back inside, blinded by my fury.

I think this may be why I dream about cats. The knowledge that they consistently defeat me, in my own garden.

Dead Silent

Gary English

'Shh. Listen'

    'What? What is it?'

    'Nothing.'

    'What?'

    'Can't you hear it?'

    'Hear what? I can't hear anything.'

    'Except.'

    'Except what?'

    'Except the silence!'

    'Well. I can't hear any noise. So I suppose I can hear silence, yeah.'

    'Don't you find it odd? The silence.'

    'I don't know. I didn't notice until you mentioned it.'

    'But we've slept here a hundred times. In this subway.'

    'Yes. We have. We have no choice.'

    'And we NEVER wake up to silence. There's a city overhead! People. Taxis. Buses. Trains. Not silence!'

    'Maybe we're dead!'

    'No. Not us. We aren't silent. Maybe they're dead!'

    'Should we go check?'

    'No. It's cold. Get back under your blankets. Go back to sleep.'

'But the dead people? The silent dead people...'
'Go back to sleep. They'll still be dead in an hour.'

Dear Katherine
Gary English

We wrote letters.
Intimate, without being personal
The structure of the page reflected in our tone
The address formed foundations at the top of the
page
Formality, I suppose, was common, then
Though we did not write 'Dear Sir or Madam,'
I called you by your name, which was dear to me
Though I did not realise how precious you were
Dear Katherine
We wrote of daily events; mundane, perhaps, to
others
With mild humour and the sweetest love of friends
With innocence and deep consideration
I marvel, now, that I never came to you
That something kept us apart
Every day, I wrote
As you became a nurse
Perhaps while I gazed at you in admiration, you
said 'I do' to him
In honesty, now, I forget
I think of you, Dear Katherine, on quiet days and
wonder
Do you remember?
At school, before you went? Your home, alone.
At sixteen years, yet never kissed or spoke of love

Such opportunity!
Yet we indulged in nothing more than scoffing cakes,
bought at the shop along the way
Vanilla slices, I recall – my first long-lasting love
Such messy cakes!
Today, I have my life and you have yours
We never meet
And when I sit in silence, as I do now, I am torn
between wishing I had kissed your neck
And feeling gratitude that I did not
For now, I have exquisite memories, untainted
Of eating cakes
And later, writing letters of daily joys and innocence
that always ended with my love
And started with
'Dear Katherine,'

Deborah in the Park
Gary English

I often lay with Deborah in the park. Kissing her
by the bush that shielded us from onlookers
We whispered words of teenage love, not knowing
what they meant, with no concept of devotion or
eternity
Distant sounds of birds and tarmac tyres played a
symphony - a soundtrack to our story
Until the day she asked: 'Do you like avocado?'
I don't know why she asked
'Do you like avocado?'
I questioned her question. This was no place for
such things
But she persisted
'Do you like Avocado?'
And so I had to admit it. I had no idea if I liked
avocado. She uttered surprise that I had never
tasted avocado. But I ate Heinz Beans and burnt
bangers. She ate avocado
And worse was to come. Her face fell and my
world collapsed when I admitted
'To be honest I don't know what avocado is. Is it
like a pear?'
We never kissed again

Happy Ghosts
Gary English

Memories shadow me
An image of you
Cutting fat from the edges of meat
Your small white dog and
its wagging tail
at your feet
Others follow
His slick grey hair and the way
he never spoke of the war
So many people
Some troubled in life
but peaceful now
She, in her blue hat and smile
watching over you, still
And the first of them all
making sure I never grow hungry
as she bangs on the door of my memory
Like I banged on her door the day she left
A procession of happy ghosts
over my shoulder
Reminding me who I am

Healed
Gary English

I know he feels like he's dead
About me
Regrets in his head
About me
For the bruising he caused
To my being
When he left
Punishing himself
And I don't tell him
I'm alright now
And I don't tell him
I'm healed
I just let him sweat in his bed
Punishing himself
For the bruises he caused

Lockdown Senses
Gary English

You are the colour of the sunrise
On deep red fences
And sparkling dew on greenest grass
Blue-grey skies with polished perfection
Pollution window-wiped away
Your heart is golden
Blanket-wrapped
And softly swaddled
Though we sometimes kick
And struggle
As infants do
A maternal wolf
Prowling
Baring teeth
To keep us safe
Locking us in
Or locking us out?
Are we prisoners
Or are we patients?

Oops
Gary English

The glass tumbled from my hand
and shattered on the tiled floor
A thousand pieces of chaos
Like my life
Like your heart when I shattered that
No time to react
I walked away
Again
To the next disaster
Simply saying
'Oops.'

Peace is Over
(advice for something that will never happen)
Gary English

The day peace breaks out around the world, don't
smile. Don't celebrate and throw your hats into the
sky, yelling, 'Peace! Peace! All war is over!'
Stand
And blink
Breathe deeply and listen
To the silence
Survey the scene
Close your eyes and breathe
And Remember
For tomorrow it will go
Peace will disappear
As wars resume
And the world returns to normal

Pleasure Pain
Gary English

I'm not sure.
Which is pleasure?
Which is pain?
Pleasure is the one we are meant to enjoy, right?
But which one is that?
I know one starts out
With 'nice' feelings
But they usually turn to hurt
The other one feels like burning, sometimes
An intense, flame soaring through my body
Raising me high
Above this dismal world
Making me scream with power
And joy
I am king!
I am king!
Are they the same?
Pleasure Pain

The Curious Case
Gary English

Often
I'm surrounded by legs
Walking by
Or standing close
In line
Mostly, I ignore them
Unless they are shapely
And then, I daren't look up!

And thieves
I see a lot of thieves
In airport baggage sheds, as I wait my turn
Slitting, unzipping, stealing precious trinkets
But they can't cut me
My skin is leather

Then, I sit alone, in hotel rooms
Peeking through a gap in wardrobe doors
I see maids and men
Again and again
It makes me blush

I often wonder why
He leaves his wife at home
To do these things
And I wish to God

He would close the wardrobe door

The Grey White Feather
Gary English

The grey white feather glided down from unseen wings.
She looked at the page.
Glided?
Was that the word?
It didn't seem to do justice to the elegant passage of the gentle whisper that floated down on wisps of air.
Glid?
The feather glid down?
That sounded ridiculous.
Yet she had written: *The goose glided down and slid on the ice, surprised not to ski and skim over the lake's surface, now frozen in the grip of winter.*
Glided it was then.
If it was good enough for a garment of feathers on a goose, it was good enough for one feather, gliding down from unseen wings.
The golden, watery sun shaded the garden. She sat shivering; waiting for the shadows to part and warm her in the weak rays of winter.
Painted reds and hues flared and changed as the light lit their tinder. It would have reminded her of the setting sun, painting over the Grand Canyon; from orange to cherry, to crimson to cedar red and a darker mahogany before allowing the blanket of night to settle over the great gorge.

Had she ever seen the Grand Canyon, these colours in her garden, painted red by her own hand and shaded by the winter sun, would have reminded her of it.

Alas, she had never seen the Grand Canyon.

Nor Uluru, that great rock standing alone in the sandstone desert of Anangu that also passes through this spectrum as the brush of sunrise sweeps softly overhead.

The garden greens stirred, too, with winter shrubs huddling round the purple heather, reminding her that life goes on,

Amongst the death, life goes on. And among the dead, the living must survive.

She put down her pen, weary and drained.

She was calm and she would write more in a while. But for a moment, as the light warmed her, now, gently, she remembered the dead. Her soft thoughts hung like dew, gently sliding down a wide leaf or stem. Like the tears trickling down her face.

The loss was unforeseen.

Unimaginable.

Yet thousands died.

Some were killed by those closest to them, who loved them to the end, yet could not hold them.

Places of sanctuary and care for the weak and old became traps. Pits of no escape. Places of medicine turned into morgues, where you dare not chance seeking help as the helpers themselves became killers, even as they died.

But this was 2020. There was no plague; no Black Death with bursting buboes and pus to carry the stench of death.

Yet, still it came. Unseen, passed by hugs and handshakes from the innocent. From nowhere.

To everywhere.

She sighed and picked up her pen.

Sipping from her china cup, she continued to write:

The grey white feather glided down from unseen wings.

Vultures
Gary English

Dry
My mouth was so dry
As I wandered in the desert
Of my barren mind
Thoughts crumbling
As dust engulfed me
Heat
And sweat
Soaking me
To the bone
As I searched the horizon of my understanding
Trying to make out shapes
That would bring the hope of familiarity
And safety
To no avail
Abandoned
Alone
Amazed at this turn of events
I wandered
Maybe in circles
Until the vultures came, finally
To feast

The Man Who Refused Sambuca
Ginni Manning

Smoke sticky from pilfered B&H, I was drinking snakebite and black. Squashed into our crowd was the local celebrity. He was drinking water despite our insistently generous offers to buy him a pint. He'd told us his full name, but we'd shortened it. In those days, if you were from Kirkby you were exotic; Mo was from Libya and we were beside ourselves with having someone new to talk to. I asked him lots of questions, not listening to his answers. In a lull, he said he needed my help. I thought about it for a second and in that moment knew it would be genius for my UCAS form. 'Yes,' I said. 'I'll marry you.' That would make me stand out amongst all the other medical school applicants and if he got to stay in the country, well, that was an added bonus. I gave him my phone number and we all toasted our engagement, except Mo who didn't want a shot of sambuca. I didn't even care that another girl told me in the queue of the chippy that he had asked her first, but she'd had to say no because she was saving herself for George Michael.

The next hungover morning, smelling of onion gravy, I realised I needed to work out what to do – I wasn't stupid, after all. I looked through the phone book and found the Citizens Advice Bureau. Some-body picked up, and I launched into my query about how to arrange my intended nuptials. There was a pause and the man said, 'I don't know who you think you've rung, love, but this is C.A.B. Garage in Maghull and that is the stupidest idea I have ever heard.' I put the phone down quickly.

Of course, the mechanic was right, but it didn't take any time to work out what might actually help. I avoided Mohammed, stayed away from the pub a couple of nights, then finally saw him and told him I had changed my mind. He looked sad but I wasn't concentrating on that, I was catching up with my fascinating social circle.

Five years later, twenty-two and still not grown up, the phone rang in my student house. There was a crackle and a faint voice, saying his name and speaking with an urgency that frightened me. A few days later my mum mentioned my friend had rung, and she had given him my number. 'Did he get hold of you? He sounded upset.' I said no and got on with my day.

Many years later and I still think about how I put the phone down in a reflexive panic before finding out what Mohammed wanted. Now I would listen carefully to what he wanted to say and his replies to any questions I had, but it's too late. There are no answers.

It won't stop...
Ginni Manning

It won't stop the time keeping of the rumbling train
It won't stop the timpani of birds
It won't stop the volcanic rise of the cakes I bake
It won't stop the casual indifference
With which I use my sister's socks

It won't stop the elastic yawn of the dog
It won't stop my creaky morning stretch
It won't stop the squeak of my teeth after sweet tea
It won't stop my cardiac tick tock
Reminding me I have a life to live

It won't stop the mint growing upright in my yard
It won't stop the briny air of the beach
It won't stop the fracture of shells underfoot
It won't stop the pale glide of the swans
On the ruffled water of the marina

It won't stop the flick flick of the TV
It won't stop the tap tap as I type these words
It won't stop the neural firework as my brain creates
It won't stop the majestic float
Of the ships sailing upstream from our huge world

Love Letter
Hannah Eynon

during the height of your reign
days
never seemed to fade

High
summer
you reeled me in

Kissing my skin
beside me
above me
beyond

Behind

Reminding me
of who I was
of who I am

baring my all
I gave in

What would the neighbours think?

I told you at the beginning
I don't do love

damaged goods

You looked at me
nodding
understood

And in that
I knew
you too

outside
we sang along
The Rolling Stones

not touching
just smoking
Getting to know each other

til it was all too much

we played with fire
and it was
the
best
we
ever
had

Now the honeymoon is over

I feel it on the breeze
as I grieve the heat

What will I do without you?

Half a house
Hannah Eynon

This
Half a house
Must
End

Terraced

Into putting on
A brave face

Pretending

We have what
It takes

I wonder

All these
Houses
That
Are
Whole

2 Up
2 Down
A Mummy and a Daddy

I wonder

If they are any happier?

Marital bliss
Mortgages
Everything
Sorted

I see
My half a house

I'd have half
My half a house
Any day

For now I know
What it takes
To become whole

Cosbie
Hannah Eynon

She heard the way I spoke
And knew

She knew
I'd Know
For it was the way I looked

This is

Close to the bone

Standing there
In the kitchen
The way women do
When the men we love
Pick up the pieces

When the men
We love
Are a product of conflict

She told me what happened
To his father

They've named their dog after him
Cosbie

A border terrier
Who takes a shine to me?

The K.O.S.B
King's Own Scottish Borders
Brought in at the start of the Troubles
1970

And she tells me
His father was shot dead
The back of the head
Close range
In a bar
He'd gone to the bathroom

And I wonder did he see it coming
In the mirror
Or did he even get that far?

Her husband
Had to leave Glasgow
On his 21st birthday
To come and identify him

Hot tears burn my face
As she tells me all this
Her American accent
An outsider to it all
Widening my eyes

Christ
A forefinger and thumb
Make the shape of a gun
As I rub my eye sockets
Bringing me back in the room

Here we are
Two women
In the kitchen
Speaking things
We don't speak
It's in our voice
What it means to love a man like that
Who've been blown to bits

Here we are
Two women
Islands away
Decades on

Doing what we do best
Picking up the pieces
Trying to keep the peace

The Promenade

Hannah Eynon

On the way home
I could tell she had been thinking about things
It's in the way she looks out the window
Sitting beside me, in her pink car seat
The seats are down in the back
Yesterday, we went to Ikea
To buy a bookcase
Kallax. £10 off
This will change my life
I'll be organised
Except, I can't get it out of the boot myself

Sunset
Along the Promenade
Scarlett says to me, over a speed bump
'See when you get coronavirus, and you get sick and
you die, what will happen to me?'
I look at her
My face
Straight
I mean business
'Scarlett. I am not going to leave you honey. Mummy
is doing all she can to keep safe. I wash my hands
and wear a mask. Keep a distance.'
She looks out the window again
Not convinced

'I promise you I'm not going to leave you, Scarlett.
I'm not going to die of Coronavirus. And anyway, I
don't think your daddy would let me. I don't think
your daddy would let me die. He wouldn't let me
in. Into Heaven.'
I have her attention now
'He wouldn't let me join him; I know he wouldn't.
Do you think your daddy would have you here left
on your own? Both your mummy and daddy dead.'
My finger, issuing a threat
A smile on my face
Scarlett looks at me and laughs.
'Noo,' she exclaims
We both laugh
'Now do you believe me? I'm not going to leave you.
Sweetheart. I'm not going to die.'
'Yes,' she nods, still knowing everyone dies someday.
I have to come up with the goods
'And do you believe your Daddy. Do you believe
him. That he won't let me in. That he's not going to
let me die?'
'Yes,' she grins
There we are now
I nod and say no more
We drive the long way home
Chasing the sun, stopping to watch it disappear
across the lough
Knowing we will sleep well tonight

Caging us together, my love and I
Caged, confined, corralled
Compacted, compressed, contained Containment as
cohabitation Compulsory not by choice
Chums together Chucked together Chained together

Together constrained Together contained Contained
in our love Our love crated Close up, closed off Close
together Claustrophobic Captive

Besties, boxed up, bound
Bundled up, battened down, brought together A
double-breasted beast
Being, not two but one, a single-bodied being
Being together Bonded together Best together
We've been together

Imprisoned, impounded, incarcerated Individualism
imploded
Interned, inside, side by side
Straight-jacketed, two as one Strapped together
Strung together Sealed together Secure, settled, safe
Homed, housebound.

Rocked to the Core

Julie

A rock-shaped head among head-shaped rocks
Hard Rock Not a cafe Rock hard Flinty Sedimentary
Rock face, hard faced, stony faced No soft landing

Head banging Banging head
Head butt, no but, yeah but
Life's knocks
Knocking me over with a feather No feathered nest
Rocks break my fall Breaking rocks Back breaking
Brake neck (I wish!)
Don't break my achy, achy heart

You rock up On the rocks On the house Cheers!
Get your rocks off You rock
Made my world rock Were my rock
Love on the rock
(Ain't no surprise)

Can't roll with the knocks Rock 'till you drop
Rock and roll, like a rolling stone
Rock shock
Hit rock bottom Bedrock Outcrop

Get up! They said Don't lose your head Heading for
the rocks Get up! They said From under that rock
Keep your head

Not a rock-shaped head
Make headway
See ahead, get ahead, be ahead
Stay ahead, way ahead, ahead of the game

My world's been rocked Shattered.
attered.

Sling Your Hook
Julie

What gives you the right to reside right here Right
now, right under my nose?
I feel like a fugitive in full view
This fickle family's found a fresh feline focus Well,
Fiddo says, FUCK OFF, Felix!
Keep away!
As dog, I'm de facto head of house I govern the
garden too
I occupy the land from the lounge to the lettuce I do
my doggy doings down there
You don't mean diddly squat
I'm authorised to oust outsiders
This 'ere's an Autonomous Dog Zone I've profiled
you, your purrs, your paws You're pussy, an
exclusion clause
You don't equate to dog Don't sniff my arse Don't
chase my tail
I'll wag it when I want Don't want all out war
Just want you to understand
We're pro canine not cat Moggie, I may be a mongrel
But I, Molly ain't no mangy mutt
Don't take the Mickey, you're no mouser Ma Maison
is mine
So sling your hook Bag-puss Alexa's allowed, but
three is a crowd You're in the dog house
No capacity for cat Don't wanna chat cat

Don't wanna catch cat having a cat nap Enjoying cat nip
Wanna be cat free.

Pumpkin
Julie

Was expecting her to be bright orange Told one day
her eyes would be
Pre-loved
Longed for during lockdown
Kitten purchased in the time of Covid Has finally
come
Has broken ranks with kith and kin
In order to begin, a new life here A Constable charcoal
cloud Dropped from the sky
Smudge of grey Bemused by her own tail
Forgetting/not knowing its attachment to her An
addendum
She sniff-tests the world
Her contentment : a Triumph Bonneville ticking
over Her hunger: signaled by seagull- like screams
Drinking from the dog's dish
Dining from a dainty dish
She dashes it against the skirting To lick the innards
clean
Polishing off a pocket-sized pouch of pate
Stretching on hind legs she scratches the window
Gleaning the garden through glass
Grey greets green
The metal dustbin reflects her doppelgänger She
duels with her double
She bites the box bearing bottled beer Cardboard

chewing cat
Pauses on paws, pads across floors
Clambers through chair legs Dashes at closing doors
Softer than a teddy
More playful than a toy Cuter than Tweetie Pie In
extremis she sprawls Cross slate kitchen tiles Seeking
cold respite She sleeps on the stairs
Feline fur fluffier than sheepskin Folds into fabric
Tail and tufts meld
Grey on grey
Into carpet, the cat vanishes

Into carpet, the cat vanishes

Lost For Words
Julie

First you made me wait
Then you made me late (for my 11 o'clock) Weighted
down with waiting
I waited some more
For words without weight
Weasel words, wasted words, worthless words
Making it worse
Words worth NOT a William!

Worthlessness washes over me
Wishing I were wasted. Wishing I would waste away.
Whilst you waste your time and mine
Whittling away my will to live
With your witless wittering, wittering on and on

Barely heard her words Hollow words
Gives her word
Never heard her draw breath As she bowled words
at me
Too many, too soon, too much, too fast, too frequent
Ill thought out
My thoughts drowned out In that wall of sound
I found
The monstrosity of verbosity
The power of words pissed away against a Brutishly
big brick-built wall

Here to help
Clumsy, cloying kindness Sensed sincerity
But sought clarity, brevity
A solution focused approach Wordless, I wait for
her words to abate Can you hear me?
I hear you loud and clear Thought I'd lost you then
You lost me long ago

Treasured Tomato
Julie

I'm plastic fantastic Oversized food
I'm red, I'm green, no colour in-between I'm flat
bottomed
Full bodied
On top, a lid with nozzle, cap attached You're
attached to me
I'm a substitute
A squishy, squashy sauce dispenser A semi-solid
surrogate
Some thought me a pepper, you knew better I'm
better than a bottle
You view me as a prop Propped upon your table top
Nothing but decoration
For your pseudo cafe-
round table; checkered cloth, corner of your kitchen
You're using me, by not using me, you haven't used
me once Sat with friends you catch up
Fill me please with ketchup I'm fond of a fondle
Invert me, squeeze me, I'll fart
I'll dribble and splutter and splatter Before I deliver
a blood red pool
A puddle upon your plate
I'm kitsch, I'm crass, I'm laughable I'm a forgettable
non-collectable
A silly souvenir
But you hang onto me, convinced I'm a work of art

Because you bought me at Tate
Down on the dock
In the shop at the end of the Shopping Show And
so you show me off
To show that you were at the show I'm all you have
to show for it
A show about consumer culture I shop, therefore
I am
I only cost a pound
You were tickled pink by me In your mind, I'm quite
a find An object found: Duchampian As the object
of your affection What is your objective?
I object to your objectifying me You relish me

Relinquish me

Release me, set me free Don't wanna be
Your treasured tomato

Sucker
Julie

I seek succour in you
You take up squatters' rights
Now I must manhandle you
Move you on
Previously I picked you Now I must unpick you My
sticky-fingers
Your vice-like grip
Limpet clinging to my back molars Back molars, now
black molars Distasteful discolouration
You fill my teeth like amalgam
My failure to stick with the programme Suck not
chew
Suck not chew Must not masticate Too late!

Sweet embedded with my bite Ephemeral evidence:
extremely chewy Flavoursome, firm favourite
Fiddly, tightly wrapped Fingernails prize you free
Parcel packed with punch Your presence, your
purpose Pure pleasure provision
You begin life, a big black block End it, a small
solitary square In communion with me
Sucked from something to nothing Recklessly, I
choose you
The chewiest of chews Choose not to chew you But
do!

Juice generating gem
Spine tingling, saliva stimulating Saccharine, sugar
sweet hit
I Soften you up
Savour you slowly
Cannot resist your resistance to me Black Jack leaves
a tell-tale stain Skid mark upon my tongue

Wotchamacallit?
Julie

Recalcitrant residue Removal required
From forefinger and thumb
Rigorously I suck both Moreish
Saliva sodden
Soft snack
Softened some more
By my Pavlovian response to The air filled
Feather light
Feet smelling
Counterfeit confected chemical cheese flavour Now
sucked to destruction
Dayglo dust dissipates Dissolving disintegrating
Digestive disappearance
Of orange phosphorescent puff Wotsit
Wots not to like?

Homage
Julie

I Know Everything's Gonna be Alright Because…
Week One:
Weakened wounded wretched wench wept Laid
upon kitchen floor
Balanced on the brink, between sink and sink no
more
Brought back by the Brummie Roller

Words of a bird lover, then another Two pigeon
fanciers, fancy that!
Absurd to have heard two birds in words
Catch the pigeon, catch the pigeon,
Prosaic pigeon praised, pronounced profound

Our Zoom room became a virtual loft Filled with
feathered friends
Seen on screen, miles apart, yet
Homed together, home from home, not home alone
Perched in rows
Portrait gallery, grid of grins Poets parroting pigeons
Soft bodies in safe hands
Loving what we love, learning to love what we love
some more, even more than we did before
Flown in wild geese, flown out NOT tamed but
taught. Tight, tidied, toned
Honed in our craft

Some birds flew away, went astray, lost along the
way Ferrying words weekly
We grew wings
Within our online world
Our loft of carrier pigeons took off Carried aloft by
writing

Prompted by prompts we promptly progressed
Penned poetry and prose
Encountered flash fiction
Creative constriction
Fly high on limited words
Sky's the limit, soar, (score that out - cliche)

Free write, free to write, writing freely, writing for
free Exercising the right to write, right minds think
alike It's right to write, anyone in their right mind
knows

Lockdown grey gave way to Golden Wonder Is it
any wonder my heart is locked down here

You do not have to be good But you can be good at
crisps Worry away a Wotsit
Crunch Monster Munch at lunch Thanks a bunch,
just a hunch
Anybody single could mingle with a Pringle
The world offers itself to your imagination We read,
we wrote, were read to

Ghosting what had gone before
A girl read aloud to her gran, who could not Gave
gran pleasure, girl gained treasure Gift of giving
Girl gone; grown to gran; goes on giving

Symbiosity of reciprocity Galvanising generosity
Gains momentum here Gracious giant gesture

We waited outside the pub Selected sweets
Tasted tentative young love, a cream slice
Tried on lucky underpants Ave you ad a go?
Ave you ad an avocado?
Soft socks, blue shirt
Mused on migrant Mohammed The marriage he
didn't manage Confronted a croc
With head of a rock
Considered a cud chewing moose Monster on the
loose
Nothing great about Fantoni Found few fans
Enjoyed his comeuppance
An elephant lands in our Zoom room Whilst goats
gloat In Llandudno

Holidays Sickness

Forced separation Job interview House move Twins
girls born A play performed
A family bereavement The school run
A car ride

London, Leicester, Liverpool Travelled to the
Troubles
Troubled not to have troubled to travel there before.
Troubled we voted to lose the loo

Virtually present
The presence of absence, absence of presence
Shadowed us
Haunted by depression, devastatingly described
Stalked by grief, love and loss
Disconcerting disconnection, dropping in, dropping
out Frozen
Not the Disney version

Learning to listen Listening to learn Yearning to hear
Words brought here
Daring to share, sharing with care
Cared that you shared, shared that we cared

A week's worth of waiting A week's widowhood
Winged in
Heading home again
For flourishing, nourishing words

Flew back for feedback Not chicken feed
No longer Frazzle fuelled
We fed in a field of familiar faces Know how good
that feeled?
Feeled good

Finger lickin good

Go on, Google Giai, Give the old girl a go
Greek Goddess Mother Earth
Giai's got it going on

A little before Fucking Attenborough Long before
Fucking Lockdown James Lovelocked down on Giai
Announcing our place in the family of things

Us and earth, self-regulatory synergy Harmless,
harmony
Visionary tranklement cabinet

Don't compete We're all unique Don't apologise
Cutthroat clearing
Mine for gems, a single line
Show me yours, I'll show you mine Show. Don't tell
Remember that. Nothing Happened Corner of Costa
Forget Costa lot coffee
Prize winning pigeons
Bred to dazzlin here, will roost there preening Cooing
to one another
Future bookshelf can't be lifted Groans under tomes
Weight of words, written by us
Willing words; not yet written; waiting for us

A dozen weeks on Miles have been flown As one we
have grown Feathers fused

No longer on mute
Together we came out as writers
Committed to write more and more and more and
more and more and more and more and more
Shit! Less is more

Meanwhile the world goes on
And somewhere deep within me tea turns to pee

The Profit To Be Made
Moon

As I stand by the socially distant pond, observing
flies gobbled down by opportune fish plucked
from the water by tornadoes of seagulls, whilst
pigeons sit like buzzards in the treetops,
I conclude life profits from death and,
when you're at the top of the food chain,
everything profits from yours.

So, I wonder
how much easier they would breathe
if I did not
and if COVID-19
will be the answer
to their prayers.

Yet, returning home, I see
my cat's desire for my existence, knowing
she'd be left to find food for herself whilst
fending off the lecherous toms, and I remember
my garden plants would be strangled
if I did not release the bindweed's hold, and
many creepy-crawlies would freeze
if I did not turn on the heat.

So, I wonder
what is the purpose

of shunning life
when, even in death,
it will never be
two metres away.

The Truth Will Out
Moon

She ran into the churchyard, high heels in hand, hardly noticing the gravel underneath. Out of breath, she headed for the burnt down bell tower. Sliding down against it, her head fell between her knees and she sobbed.

Only hours before, Nadia had picked out her outfit. She was tempted to wear white just for the devilment. Perhaps the trouser-suit or the maxi dress. But then she spotted the red jumpsuit. Perfect. Isn't that what they all thought of her anyway: the scarlet woman? So why not own it?

When she arrived at the hotel, Allan and Michelle stood in the lobby, arm in arm. Nadia conceded Michelle looked stunning in her wedding dress. The bitch looked so smug. It made Nadia hate her all the more but, for now, it was all fake smiles and pleasantries.

'Nice outfit,' Allan said pointedly. Nadia just thought, '1-0 to me,' and headed straight for the bar.

It wasn't always like this. For a time, they hadn't been able to keep their hands off each other but, as soon as their families learned of the relationship, Christian united with Muslim to keep their offspring apart.

So here she was, dancing with some random fella who couldn't believe his luck. They were dancing so closely; she could feel the stiffness in his pants. A girl like her wasn't going to be short of attention. Even the godawful cover band were soon belting out 'The Lady in Red'. This clearly upset someone for, not long after, it was Rick Astley's 'Never Gonna Give You Up'. The jibe was not lost on Nadia. Casting aside her dancing partner, she marched over to the newly married couple.

'Are you fucking joking me!' she demanded. 'Never gonna give you up? You fucking dumped me in a heartbeat!'

'You're deluded,' Allan responded. 'You were only a one-nighter!'

Nadia shook her head. 'Not you, fuckhead! Her!'

It must've been the shortest marriage on record.

Fallen
Moon

Inspired by The Grand Finale by Tim Craig

Of all the things I've seen, that was the most shocking. There was blood right up to the windows and poor Ethel lay on her side, body collapsed in on itself, her legs twisted around each other. Scarcely alive, her screams shook the building whenever she tried moving her not-inconsiderable weight. Being in such a state meant just one thing and I held back a tear at the thought of it. Yet, when I re-opened my eyes, the vet was already inserting the catheters.

Such an abrupt ending was ill-fitting for the patience she'd been famed for. Even the grace that returned to her body as she fell into her eternal sleep was short lived. For next, they were focussing in on the problem of moving her. It was not a job for the weak willed, but it was imperative to do so, as his body lay crushed underneath.

With just his feet sticking out, it was like something out of a Looney Tunes cartoon, except no one was laughing. This was real life, where people died when an elephant fell on them. But how? The staircase would be too narrow and how would she have got onto the roof anyway? And even if you worked out how she got up there, it still left the question of why? Yet the evidence was unmistakable: Ethel had fallen right on top of The Great Fantoni and there was no pulling a rabbit out of a hat for this one.

Blue Shirt
Moon

It was not the shirt so much. It was stylish enough, coming from Top Man. It was the way you wore it with only the bottom three buttons done up, your hairy chest for all to see. I could even see your nipple ring. For a man of your age, it was a bit much - even for Canal Street! So I asked you to do the shirt up. Not for the last time, you told me not to be such a prude. I decided not to argue but, really, you were over fifty. You should've covered yourself up.

Then, settling into our comfy life together, you developed quite a paunch. So, it was just as well the shirt was slimming, with its shading at the sides. It even had a fashionable Celtic design on the sleeves. You looked quite decent in it – decent enough for our Civil Partnership – when you did the buttons up.

Of course, when you were stuck in your wheel-chair, it was the bottom buttons that weren't done up. It remained a favourite for special occasions though. Mind you, it wasn't the best of looks, with your face all puffed up from the steroids. I did try to tell you, but you weren't interested. But, really, I think you would've looked better in one of your pullovers or polo-necks.

Was I beginning to dress you then? God, that was awful. I seemed to hurt you with every touch. I was utterly clueless. I was glad when you went into the hospice. But I guess they found it too hard to dress you too, as you were always in your pyjamas; with the buttons all undone and hairy chest for all to see.

I can't remember now what outfit you were wearing when you were cremated but it wasn't that blue shirt. That's still in the wardrobe; hanging there in the darkness, buttons all undone. I can still smell your scent on it. I think it misses you as much as I do.

Bitter Aftertaste
Moon

How was I to know? I just thought it might be lemon flavour or something. After all, yesterday was Shrove Tuesday. We had fabulous pancakes. I prefer banana and Nutella but where do you find banana out in the Arctic? That's more the Caribbean. So we had them drizzled with lemon and sugar. Brian packed it. He's thoughtful like that. Mind you, he couldn't fight his way out a wet paper bag but I'm glad we brought him instead of Jack. Jack wouldn't have thought to bring lemon and sugar. It would've been all scientific instruments with him. Probably even a Bunsen burner and what use is a Bunsen burner out here?

So, yeah, seeing it there, it reminded me of the slushies we get back home. Raspberry was always my favourite but, you know, when presented to me for free, I'm not gonna turn down a lemon one either. I thought it would be refreshing. How was I to know any different? It's the first time I've been on one of these trips.

Obviously, I did think twice before scooping it up, but beggars can't be choosers. And, besides, I still haven't forgiven Peter for helping himself to all the Daim bars. There was no way I was letting him have all the slushie as well. I don't know why we even brought him. He's almost as thick as he is fat.

Still, he was the first to me with the water. I have to give him that. I can still taste it though and it still makes me gag. But how was I to know? I thought it would be like a lemon slushie.

Restrictions
Moon

It's surreal not knowing when I'll see my friends again. Having a wander around the shops feels weird – like an act of courage in fact - and I'm not supposed to meet up with my neighbour at home or in the garden. We're not even supposed to meet up in public, so we can't go down the pub or meet up at the cinema either – not that I have any idea when I last went to the cinema. And I don't drink either.

To make matters worse, me and my best friend are separated by the Mersey but neither of us are supposed to use public transport socially and we don't own a car. So not only are we restricted by geography and the government, but by our knowledge of technology.

I have no idea how to set up a meeting on Zoom. Instead, we use Facebook Messenger. I am glad to see her face as well as hear her voice but the novelty of face filters and the joke about her shrinking so small are well-worn now. We've also noticed that the filter of technology somehow limits the conversation. So instead of passing hours talking about nothing, I find myself clock watching with nothing to talk about.

On top of that, I have sinusitis and so have been instructed to get as much fresh air as possible. Yet I am limited to how far I can walk and seeing the same thing every day soon got boring. I'm fortunate

I live across the road from the park, though, and can make friends with the greenery but I'm no Prince Charles. So, some days I never hear the sound of my own voice, let alone anyone else's.

The ducks are amusing, though, and are wonderful to watch in flight but soon they'll be flying south for the winter, while I will be left in the cold.

2020's vision of Pride
Garnett 'Ratte' Frost

It should have been today. This was the day we waged our annual war on hate.

Locking my bedroom door, I excavate my little flags from the back of the bottom drawer. Curtains drawn, listening for footsteps on the stairs. I close my eyes, remembering last year's Pride.

Rain glistened on the dull pavements as our river of rainbows ambled through the city. Whistles and cheers filling the sodden air. Flags were flung around, as much to try and dry them as in support.

From under a canopy of umbrellas, phones watched high heels slipping on slick tarmac and make-up melting down faces.

No one was going to dull our sparkle. Not the preaching placards or overzealous TERFs. We were here, the united queer, minorities supporting each other against hate.

Fears of being outted were pushed to the back of my mind as my trans and rainbow flags merged with the rest. Temporarily I felt free of pigeonholes that insist you must be only one thing or another, and judgements about how you can or can't live.

Checking my door was definitely locked, I wave

my flags as I watch a silent montage of clips from previous Prides on YouTube. Wishing I was safe to just be openly me.

Love is Love, but fear is fear.

Coronial Birth

Garnett 'Ratte' Frost
Tears tumble over hot cheeks,
wanting comfort
needing confinement.

Eyes confronted with anxious masks,
microscopic menaces
medical miracles.

Encased in plastic armour, unhuggable,
thoughts unknowable
results unthinkable.
Weak voices cry out
unanswered.

Llandudno Lockdown
Garnett 'Ratte' Frost

'There she goes again.' Carys tutted as her mam wandered across the boggy field towards her.

'Who, love?'

'That Gwen by there, you were right, Mam, nothing but trouble. Fancy going to Llandudno for a "day out" during lockdown.' Carys plucked a flower from the tall grass as they watched Gwen trying to scale the dry-stone wall.

'I like Llandudno,' her mam sighed, studying the town below. 'Some tidy Victorian buildings, and the beach...'

'Beach? Sandy shingle is not a beach. Rhiannon said they were crossing the road without checking for cars, trampling over people's gardens, flouting the two-metre rule and masks? Forget masks,' Carys scoffed as Gwen tumbled onto Rhiannon.

'I saw the police chasing them. Gwen's lucky they haven't given her an ASBO.'

'They'll give her more than that if they realise, she's the one who led the raid on that school the other week.' Carys sneered, unwilling to admit her part in that invasion.

Her mam shook her head, 'I do worry about you, peer pressure and all that-'

'You know I'm no sheep, following Gwen blindly into bother.' Carys rolled her eyes as a falcon circled overhead. 'Besides, Rhiannon said the shops are still shut.'

'Love, I don't think they'd do stuff in your size.' Her mam mumbled, biting the head off a nearby flower.

'Why not? They use enough of our fleece to make their clothes, don't they?'

The Monster
Garnett 'Ratte' Frost

I used to cower under my quilt as it skittered across the carpet towards my bed. Spiny legs nudged toys out of the way as it made its nest beneath me. Feeding my nightmares.

Now I understand why it hid. It must have known about the invisible monsters lurking on unmasked faces and unwashed hands. The threat of infection turning partners into untouchable pixels, hugs into hazards and coughs into killers.

These nights, when it scurries to safety below my bed, it makes more space so I can hide there too.

Self-service
Garnett 'Ratte' Frost

Cashiers swipe items through their Perspex cages, unwilling or unable to speak to customers. Hiding the yellow labels beneath the bread, I queue for self-service. I know it's an unwritten rule you avoid self-service if you have discounted stuff, but after five months around the kids, I needed human contact.

I pick the till nearest the gaggle of staff and excavate my first yellow label. Hoping they will appreciate the toothy grin printed on my mask.

The item scans without a problem. Envy festers in my chest with each successful beep whilst others call for help.

Not a single error, not even a wrong price. The one and only time I've ever wanted to have to call staff over...

Defeated, I tip the coppers out of my wallet pouring them down the till's plastic gullet before slowly packing my bags. I'll have to try again at another checkout. At least my wallet felt as light as my bank account now.

#Holiday (Radio play)
Garnett 'Ratte' Frost

Scene One

Sounds of coffee machines hissing, quiet chatter and a spoon scraping the inside of a paper cup. Distant sounds of city vehicles pass by outside.

Si: (Mutters to himself) Not the selfie queen.

High heeled footsteps walk closer across a tiled floor before stopping.

Jade: Si? What are you doing here?

Si: It's a coffee shop, Jade.

Jade: Obviously… Why you putting a mask on? You don't need to wear one in here.

Si: (His voice slightly muffled) Cause I've finished my coffee. I'm not risking catching anything this time either.

Jade: Know anyone who got it? Of course not. It's just media hype. Anyway… Heard what happened? My followers are telling me to take the bosses to court. False drizzle.

Si: You mean dismissal. One of them found out you were on holiday when you were pulling a sickie, didn't they?

Jade: A week in a manky caravan in Boggy Regis with 'im and his kids. Benidorm is a holiday Si. Wales is a punishment-

Si: Thought it was Benidorm?

Jade: Used last year's selfies. Can't have people knowing I've ever been in a caravan.

Si: I like Wales, some good hiking trails.

Jade: Anyhow, you're looking tanned.

Si: It's from my daily walks. Gotta keep fit. This is the first time I've been back for a coffee since they shut our office.

Jade: Weren't you like sick or something a couple of weeks ago?

Si: Luckily wasn't the virus-

Jade: Telling you it's not real. Laugh all

you want, Si. They've stopped stuff like flour and toilet rolls and hair dye to cause panic and make people spend more money online. It's a fact... Oh my actually! Look at my roots! I'm sure they didn't look that bad earlier.

Si: Jade, you've got a pretty face. Why do you try to look like Donald Duck's jaundiced sister in your selfies?

Jade: My hair's not that bad!

Si: What?

Jade: I'm not showing my roots on my late lunch latte selfie.

Si: Your late what? Why does everything have to be put online with you? Live a little.

Jade: You think you're so clever.

Si: No. It's just I'm not the one who messed up going on holiday whilst claiming to be ill during a global pandemic.

Jade: I told you-

Si: I mean if I'd spent three glorious weeks

on Gibraltar, when I was claiming I was sick, I wouldn't post photos online and tag them #Holiday.

Jade: Gibraltar? What? Have you been away-

A chair is dragged out

Si: A daily walk is a daily walk, wherever you happen to be. See you around, Jade.

Man's footsteps walk onto the street; vehicle engines grow louder.

End of Scene One

Babysitting Sam
Garnett 'Ratte' Frost

Peeking through my porch window as, still in her mismatched pjs, she stuffed unmasked children around bulging suitcases, trying not to knock their iPads out of their zombified hands. With a hacking cough he brought out the grubby carrier, its tiny occupant still snoozing amidst the early morning shouting and swearing. Taipei, Tenerife, Torquay, Talacre, somewhere, anywhere that wasn't 18 Dreary Lane, even for a weekend.

Dumping the carrier between the bins and their beaten-up S-MAX, his flipflops slapped the tarmac driveway as he hurried back inside for the bag containing the money and chargers. Slamming the front door, he tossed the bag at her as he got in, not bothering to move his leather jacket from the seat. He almost rear ended the bin lorry as he wheel-spun onto the road.

Trundling my bin to the pavement, I noticed the discarded carrier. They were already out of sight. What was I supposed to do now? I didn't have a number for them.

'Not called Kevin, is he?' The bin man scoffed behind his mask as I cradled the mucky carrier.

He didn't look like a Kevin. If he was mine, I'd call him Sam, after my grandad. The well-worn stained yellow onesie didn't suit his olive skin.

After a decade of trying, this was the closest to a family I'd gotten. Maybe they'd enjoy their holiday so much they'd forget about him. Then he could be my Sam, filling the house with life and mess.

He'd love the back bedroom. He could watch the sunset whilst I read him stories. I'd paper the walls with jungle print, so we could pretend to be lions and tigers and monkeys. I could almost feel him clinging to my hand as I took him to his first day at school. Cheering him as he played sports, maybe he'd be team captain like Grandad. Watching him collect a degree, maybe even a masters or doctorate like Mum. I wondered if he'd find a nice girl to settle down with nearby, or, I suppose a nice guy, hopefully have his own kids either way. Sam, my Sam, my precious Sam.

Nudging the dummy back in his mouth I barely notice a car pull up opposite. A petrol-blue haired boy crawled from the back seat, tucking his nose under his t-shirt's collar as he yanked Sam from my arms.

'Honestly, he'd forget his name if I didn't remind him.' She hollered from the passenger seat as the kids tried to strap the carrier in, waking the baby who started to cry. 'Thanks for babysitting Simba.'

Simba? 'I'd have looked after him!' I promised.

'Don't tempt me to say yes.' She laughed as he did a ten-point turn, killing my gnomes again.

Bubbles of Joy

Garnett 'Ratte' Frost

I watch
translucent
spheres dance on
the draft from
my window.
Floating,

spinning.
Their skins a
riot of fragile
rainbows.

Each filmy
globe captures
my breath.
I blow

harder, forcing
them towards
the pimpled
ceiling.

Hugging
their soapy
siblings as they
flutter towards
me. Landing

on my
skin before
they finally

pop

Plague Birds
Garnett 'Ratte' Frost

Smoky scars maul the cloudless sky
Carrying fresh plague on metal wings
From distant shores in recycled air
Profits are pursued at any price
The virus prepares to disembark

Has a Month Ever Felt So Long?

Vickie Rowell

Has a month ever felt so long as it has recently?
This Pandemic is making me rather twitchy.
The days are never ending,
Sleep, eat and repeat.
Has a month ever felt so long?
Same shit different day,
New rules come into play.
Face covering on the bus to work,
People fighting for items in the shop.
My mind is blown,
No toilet paper, no pasta,
Not even a bottle of hand sanitizer.
Oh, the insanity of it all,
When will it be over?
Has a month ever felt so long before?
We've reached the month of my birthday.
Never had one like this before.
The days are still never ending,
Maybe it's a good thing I'm turning thirty-seven.
I wonder if things will ease by then,
Maybe I'll be allowed out,
Not out out,
But actually out.
Has a month ever felt so long?
My son leaves primary.
No party for him as a leaver,

It makes me shiver.
No shirts to be signed,
Poor lad is out of his mind.
All the talk of mums and their past experiences
and he leaves with Covid 19 memories.
He will be a lockdown child,
The leaving primary will not be as wild.

Has a month ever felt so long?
It is the height of summer.
We are now allowed out,
Yes, allowed out out but,
With a mask in hand.
We are leaving Liverpool for London,
Road trip in a van,
Seeing my family after five months,
I have goose bumps.
This year will be one I won't forget,
September has arrived,
Perfect time to start afresh.

I'm Coming Home
Vickie Rowell

I'm coming home
Eleven years I have lived here,
my son in tow too.
He needs to spread his wings,
and I need my mum like glue.
I have fought long and hard,
had years of being alone.
Now its time to shout aloud,
'I'm coming home.'

Nothing against Liverpool,
The City is unique.
The people are so lovely,
As well as the scenery.
You have the famous Albert Dock,
Museums at hand too.
Beaches a bus ride away,
I wish I could stay.

A year ago I decided it would be best,
Best for the pair of us.
Secondary school for Lewis,
He is excited to start a new.
London is very busy,
Plenty of scenery too.
I look at Lewis and see his smile,

I'm sure this will be worthwhile.
Nervous, he is, yes
But I know he will do his best.

The Bird
Vickie Rowell

You shoo me along,
Which isn't nice.
Maybe I want what you have:
That dish of fried rice.
I see you look at it in admiration,
Does it give you that same satisfaction?
It must do, as you hold it with dear life.
Like I'm going to swoop it from you,
So I can feed my pigeon wife.
I have a family you see,
Yes that is right.
They are hiding,
Humans give them a fright.

Why do you cover your head and crouch?
Like we are going to land on your snout.
We fly low,
We fly high,
It depends what is in our sight.

Don't shout or scream when we come near,
We are all hungry let me make that clear.
Don't blame me if I go on attack,
Those donuts you carry are my favourite snack.
The sugar-coated rings,
Puts a sprint in my wings.

We are all here to survive this 2020 life,
Please stop giving us pigeons strife.

Author's Biographies

Ange Woolf is a Liverpool born poetry writer, who until recently, was sharing her writing with only a small number of people; joining Writing on the Wall has encouraged her to leap into the deep end of the writing pool and there'll be no turning back now! With an academic background in Psychology and English Literature, along with nearly 30 years of disability support, mental health and academic mentoring, she has gone on to combine her twin loves of Writing and Psychological thinking, to create a draft working model for a future venture that will incorporate her passions and create a service for the purpose of supporting people to find the best versions of themselves. Ange has been part of the Poised Pen writing group from Liverpool for the past few years, sharing writing with other like-minded souls, but Writing on the Wall's Write Minds anthology will be her first published work. Ange has also recently launched a writing page on Facebook called, 'a word slinging Woolf' and is currently looking forward to spending more time writing, building support for her page and creating a future life that contains more of what makes her feel purposeful and content.

Bretta Kane was born and still lives in Liverpool. One of 8 children her parents, whose own education was cut short by illness and the second world war, encouraged and inspired her love of reading and writing. Retiring from working in Finance after 30 years, Bretta became a full time guardian of a young child which has given her the opportunity to focus on her creative writing and the Write Minds sessions and workshops have provided a safe and supportive space for her to develop and share her work. This is the first time she has had any work published Bretta's other love is singing and she is a member of an a cappella choir, Vocality, which has afforded her many memorable opportunities to sing at amazing venues and events. Highlights have included the opening of the Everyman Theatre and the premier of the Blue Planet television programme at the BBC Worldwide Showcase event where Vocality, along with several other local choirs, sang the backing for the Hans Zimmer theme tune.

Danielle McLauren (aka The Half Pint Poet) is a Liverpool born writer and theatre-maker. Currently writing her autobiographical one-woman-show, for which she received a Seed Commission from the Liverpool Everyman New Works Department, Danielle also has a collection of poetry to accompany the play, which she hopes to publish alongside the production. Recent achievements include being awarded Woman of the Week by We Want Women Liverpool, for her spoken word piece about period shame, and being commissioned to write a poem by

Altru Drama, to be performed in primary schools across the country, as part of anti-bullying week.

Deborah Williams is a Liverpool born writer. She first had a collaborative play under the Everyman's writing programme performed by the youth theatre. Since then she has continued to hone her writing skills and has completed the Write to work programme with WOW, with her short stories published in the anthology Jigsaw. She has had her first foray into essay writing published in the anthology, SS Orbita to Orbital, a look at the musical influences of the Windrush generation. Her main interests lie in writing for children and is looking to have her children's novel published.

Gary English has combined a career in education with work in journalism for over twenty years. His writing has appeared in sports publications and local newspapers in the Merseyside area. Having recently branched out into poetry and prose, Gary has had writing published in a series of anthologies entitled 'Nonsensically Challenged'. He is currently compiling two anthologies of his own work, entitled 'Stories from My Life' and 'Love, Lies and Limericks'. Gary's message to the world is: "I come in peace. Take me to your reader

Hannah Eynon is a Northern Irish Writer. In her own words, Hannah slows time down to capture and see what really matters.

Julie appreciates art. Lives in Liverpool. Partial to practicing poetry.

Moon is a genderqueer artist with a focus on the written word and they also take an interest in writing itself. My writing has been published in The Guardian and two previous WoW anthologies. I am grateful to WoW - particularly Lauren Buxton and Deborah Morgan - for providing this opportunity to develop my writing. It instilled a confidence in me about expressing my mad ideas and more personal concerns. With the limitations brought on by the pandemic, these rays of hope could not have come at a more crucial time in my life.

Garnett 'Ratte' Frost is a dyslexic transman and wire artist with an English degree. The nickname Ratte comes from riding matt black motorcycles (known as rat bikes). He currently co-facilitates a local LGBTQI+ creative writing group. He has been published in Writing on the Wall's TranScripts and Moving Foreword anthologies. Much of his work is viewable online under the username Garnet69Frost and Ratte. He is working on a LGBT+ short story anthology and series of fantasy-horror novels beginning with

Out of Sight.

Ginni Manning is a playwright, theatre maker and writer from Liverpool, U.K. She is a facilitator and writer for Writing on the Wall and volunteers as an assistant writer with Action Transport Theatre Young Writers group. In 2020, Ginni was chosen by the Everyman Theatre in Liverpool to be part of the Sphinx30 Theatre Female Playwright Development Programme, in which she receives a commission to write a full length play and attends masterclasses with a network of 30 other female playwrights nationally. She is a member of Write Local Play Global, the playwright organisation associated with Assitej (The International Association of Theatre for Children and Young Audiences) and performed at the Assitej 2017 Cradle of Creativity. She co-wrote Dipalo, the Assitej Award winning play, with Lalu Mokuku, a theatre maker from South Africa, which is being published in 2020 and produced in 2021.

Vickie Rowell is 37 years old and she absolutely loves writing, be it short stories or poetry. Vickie first started writing poetry when she was 13. She remembers sitting in the school canteen smiling to herself because she made my piece rhyme, that image has stuck to me ever since. Her love of poetry came from airing her emotions. Each downfall she has taken is written as either a poem or short story. Vickie has had her work published in pamphlets from my Creative Writing course that she had attended In Liverpool. She also has some poems published online, on The Organic Poet website.

Afterword

Congratulations to all those who participated in What's Your Story? Write Minds, for producing such high-quality writing and being generous enough to share their stories with us. The impact of the Lockdowns on mental health has been well documented. But behind the statistics are people, many without a voice. We salute the honesty and bravery, and offer our thanks to these writers, and hope that their amazing work will offer hope to others who are have found their wellbeing has suffered during the pandemic. Special thanks to Unison for their support for this project.

Writing on the Wall is a dynamic Liverpool-based community organisation, which celebrates writing in all its forms. We hold an annual festival and a series of year-round projects, working with a broad and inclusive definition of writing that embraces literature, creative writing, journalism and nonfiction, poetry, songwriting and storytelling. We work with local, national and international writers whose work provokes controversy and debate, engaging all of Liverpool's many diverse communities in order to promote and celebrate both individual and collective creativity.

Our creative writing projects support health, wellbeing and personal development, and if you have a story to tell and would like to take part in one of our writing projects, or perhaps work with us to develop a new initiative, please do get in touch. We'd love to hear from you.

Madeline Heneghan and Mike Morris, Co-Directors
info@writingonthewall.org.uk
www.writingonthewall.org.uk
0151 703 0020
@wowfest